101 HITS FOR BUSKERS
BOOK 4 · Bb EDITION

Wise Publications
London/New York/Sydney/Cologne

Music Sales Limited
78 Newman Street, London W1P 3LA, England
Music Sales Limited
27 Clarendon Street, Artarmon, Sydney, NSW 2064, Australia.

This book © Copyright 1980 by
Wise Publications
ISBN 0.86001.748.6
Order No. AM 26568

Arranged by: Frank Booth

Cover Illustration: David English

Music Sales complete catalogue lists thousands
of titles and is free from your local music
book shop, or direct from Music Sales Limited.
Please send 25p in stamps for postage to
Music Sales Limited, 78 Newman Street, London W1P 3LA.

Printed and bound in Great Britain by William Clowes (Beccles)
Limited, Beccles and London

1
Bright Eyes

Words and music by Mike Batt

2
Can't Smile Without You

Words and music by Chris Arnold, David Martin and Geoff Morrow

3
I Love You And Don't You Forget It

Lyric by Al Stillman
Music by Henry Mancini

4
The Entertainer

Music by Scott Joplin

5
Candle In The Wind

Words and music by Elton John and Bernie Taupin

6
Rocket Man

Words and music by Elton John and Bernie Taupin

7
There's A Whole Lot Of Loving

Words and music by Chris Arnold, David Martin and Geoff Morrow

8
Year Of The Cat

Words and music by Al Stewart and Peter Wood

9
Something Old, Something New

Words and music by Tony Macaulay, Roger Cook and Roger Greenaway

10
Proud Mary

Words and music by John C Fogerty

11
Talking In Your Sleep

Words and music by Roger Cook and Bobby Wood

12
Cottonfields

Words and music by Huddie Ledbetter

13
Taboo

Words by S K Russell
Spanish words and music by Margarita Lecuona

14
The Deadwood Stage (Whip-Crack-Away)

Words by Paul Francis Webster
Music by Sammy Fain

15
Sweet And Gentle (Me Lo Dijo Adela)

English words by George Thorn
Music by Otilio Portal

16
That'll Be The Day

Words and music by Norman Petty, Buddy Holly and Jerry Allison

17
La Cucaracha

Words and music: Traditional

18
House Of The Rising Sun

Words and music: Traditional

19
Nobody Knows The Trouble I've Seen

Words and music: Traditional

20
Without You

Words and music by Peter Ham and Tom Evans

21
Mexican Hat Dance

Words and music: Traditional

O - lay!

22
Lavender Blue

Words and music: Traditional

23
Hava Nagila

Words and music: Traditional

24
Together We Are Beautiful

Words and music by Ken Leray

25
Sexy Eyes

Words and music by Bob Mather, Keith Stegall & Chris Waters

26
Take That Look Off Your Face

Words by Don Black
Music by Andrew Lloyd Webber

27
It's A Great Day For the Irish

Words and music by Roger Edens

28
On Top Of Old Smokey

Words and music: Traditional

29
Alone Again (Naturally)

Words and music by Raymond O'Sullivan

30
Pearl's A Singer

Words and music by Ralph Dino, John Sembello, Jerry Leiber and Mike Stoller

31
Mr Bojangles

Words and music by Jerry Jeff Walker

32
Escape (The Pina Colada Song)

Words and music by Rupert Holmes

33
You'll Never Get To Heaven (If You Break My Heart)

Music by Burt Bacharach
Words by Hal David

34
Anyone Who Had A Heart

Words by Hal David
Music by Burt Bacharach

35
A Song For You

Words and music by Leon Russell

36
There But For Fortune

Words and music by Phil Ochs

37
You Need Hands

Words and music by Max Bygraves

38
April Love

Words by Paul Francis Webster
Music by Sammy Fain

39
Be My Love

Words by Sammy Cahn
Music by Nicholas Brodszky

40
Because You're Mine

Words by Sammy Cahn
Music by Nicholas Brodszky

41
Chattanooga Choo Choo

Words by Mack Gordon
Music by Harry Warren

42
Better Love Next Time

Words and music by Steve Pippin, Johnny Slate and Larry Keith

43
Frankie And Johnny

Words and music: Traditional

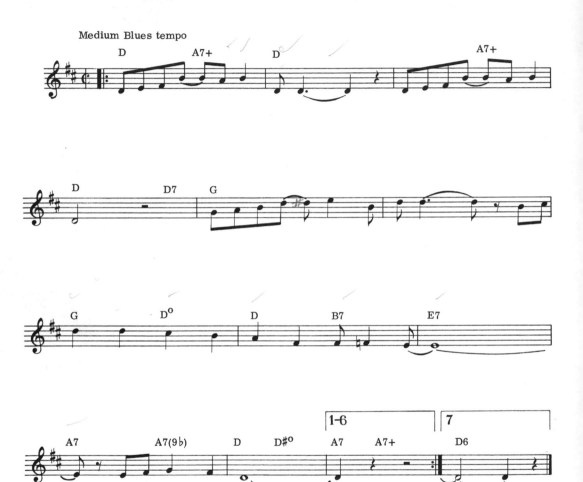

44
A Certain Smile

Words by Paul Francis Webster
Music by Sammy Fain

45
Nola

Words and music: Traditional

46
Sometimes When We Touch

Words and music by Dan Hill and Barry Mann

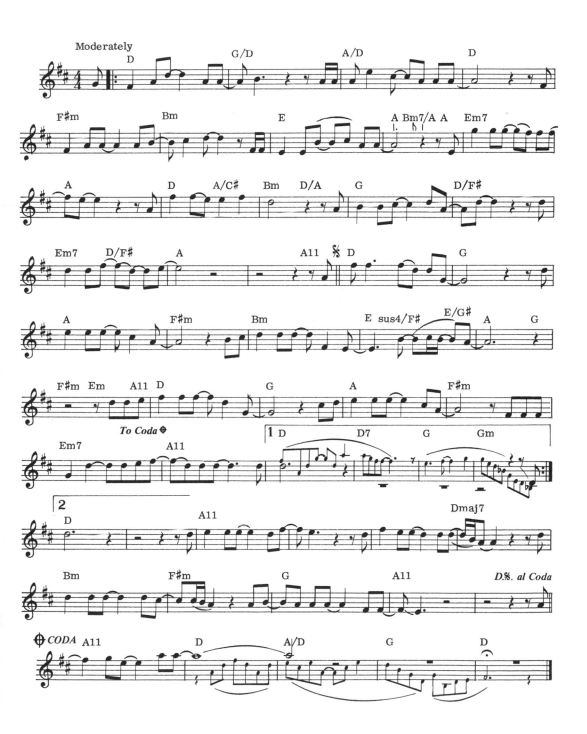

47
Clair

Words and music by Raymond O'Sullivan

48
You're In My Heart

Words and music by Rod Stewart

49
Don't Make Me Over

Lyric by Hal David
Music by Burt Bacharach

50
Money, Money

Words by Fred Ebb
Music by John Kander

51
I'll Never Fall In Love Again

Words by Hal David
Music by Burt Bacharach

52
I Say A Little Prayer

Lyric by Hal David
Music by Burt Bacharach

53
Do That To Me One More Time

Words and music by Toni Tennille

54
Please Don't Go

Words and music by H. W. Casey and R. Finch

55
How About You

Words by Ralph Freed
Music by Burton Lane

56
Raindrops Keep Falling On My Head

Words by Hal David
Music by Burt Bacharach

57
She Believes In Me
Words and music by Steve Gibb

58
It Happened In Monterey

Words by Billy Rose
Music by Mabel Wayne

59
Whatever Will Be Will Be (Que Sera, Sera)

Words and music by Jay Livingston and Ray Evans

60
Little Brown Jug

Words and music: Traditional

61
Love Makes The World Go 'Round

Words and Music by Bob Merrill

62
Ramona

Lyric by L Wolfe Gilbert
Music by Mabel Wayne

63
Santa Claus Is Comin' To Town

Words by Haven Gillespie
Music by J. Fred Coot

64
Softly As I Leave You

Original words by A. de Vita; English lyric by Hal Shaper
Music by G Calabrese

65
Toot, Toot, Tootsie!

Words and music by Gus Kahn, Ernie Erdman, Dan Russo, Ted Fiorito

66
Somewhere My Love

Words by Paul Francis Webster
Music by Maurice Jarre

67
Once In A While

Words by Bud Green
Music by Michael Edwards

68
Do You Know The Way To San Jose

Words by Hal David
Music by Burt Bacharach

69
Wishin' And Hopin'

Lyric by Hal David
Music by Burt Bacharach

70
This Guy's In Love With You

Words by Hal David
Music by Burt Bacharach

71
Maybe This Time

Music by John Kander
Lyrics by Fred Ebb

72
My Colouring Book

Music by John Kander
Lyrics by Fred Ebb

* on second time

73
Cabaret

Lyrics by Fred Ebb
Music by John Kander

74
Wives And Lovers

Words by Hal David
Music by Burt Bacharach

75
Something

Words and music by George Harrison

76
Here Comes The Sun

Words and music by George Harrison

77
Song For Guy

By Elton John

78
Tryin' To Get The Feeling Again

Words and music by David Pomeranz

79
Don't It Make My Brown Eyes Blue

Words and music by Richard Leigh

80
Day By Day

Music by Stephen Schwartz
Lyrics by John Michael Tebelak

81
I Don't Know Why (I Just Do)

Words by Roy Turk
Music by Fred E. Ahlert

82
Hurt

Words and music by Jimmie Crane and Al Jacobs

83
Moonglow

Words and music by Will Hudson, Eddie de Lange and Irving Mills

84
Fools Rush In

Lyrics by Johnny Mercer
Music by Rube Bloom

85
Come Fly With Me

Lyrics by Sammy Cahn
Music by Jimmy Van Heusen

86
Put Your Head On My Shoulder

Words and music by Paul Anka

87
Ain't Misbehavin'

Words by Andy Razaf
Music by Thomas Waller and Harry Brooks

88
Fever

Words and music by John Davenport & Eddie Cooley

89
To Know You Is To Love You

Words and music by Phil Spector

90
Let The Heartaches Begin

Words and music by Tony Macauley and John Macleod

91
Aquarius

Words by James Rado and Gerome Ragni
Music by Galt MacDermot

92
Twenty-Four Hours From Tulsa

Words and music by Burt Bacharach and Hal David

93
We Don't Talk Anymore

Words and music by Alan Tarney

Last time rpt. to chorus
and fade ad-lib.

94
Weekend In New England

Words and music by Randy Edelman

95
You Light Up My Life
Words and music by Joe Brooks

96
I Write The Songs

Words and music by Bruce Johnston

97
Ships

Words and music by Ian Hunter

98
I Can't Stop Loving You

Words and music by Billy Nicholls

99

Gimme! Gimme! Gimme! (A Man After Midnight)

Words and music by Benny Andersson and Bjorn Ulvaeus

100
One Day At A Time

Words and music by Marijohn Wilkin and Kris Kristofferson

101
Thank You For The Music

Words and music by Benny Andersson and Bjorn Ulvaeus